Back to Basics

SCIENCE

for 10–11 year olds

Godfrey Hall

Your pulse

When you exercise you use up more energy. Your heart, blood and lungs all have to work harder. You can see this by measuring your pulse.

Hold the inside of your wrist with two fingers and press down. You should be able to feel your pulse.

Use a timer or the second hand of a watch. What is your pulse rate over a minute?

Normal rate [   ] beats per minute.

Fill in this chart doing each activity for two minutes before taking your pulse.

Activity	Pulse rate
Run on the spot	
Lie down	
Walk on the spot	
Clap	
Jump up and down	

Now put these activities in order, starting with the slowest pulse rate.

1 ....

2 ....

3 ....

4 ....

5 ....

Smoking

Smoking is bad for you. It can make you cough and lose your breath. Some people get lung cancer from smoking as they get older.

Read the information about **Smoking**.

> Cigarettes contain nicotine, tar and carbon monoxide. Nicotine takes seven seconds to get to the brain. It increases the heartbeat and blood pressure. The tar in cigarettes causes lung cancer. Carbon monoxide reduces the amount of oxygen that can get into the blood. It is harmful to people with bad hearts and women expecting babies.

Answer these questions.

1   Give three reasons why smoking is bad for you.

   ....

   ....

   ....

2   What does carbon monoxide do?

   ....

3   Why do cigarette packets have a health warning on them?

   ....

Answer these questions.
Circle the correct answer from the brackets.

1   You can't buy cigarettes until the age of (15, 16, 17).

2   Tobacco adverts have been banned on television since (1970, 1990, 1965).

3   (300, 10, 200) people who smoke die every day.

4   ($\frac{1}{4}$, $\frac{1}{2}$, $\frac{1}{10}$) of all 15 year olds smoke one cigarette each week.

Personal health

It is very important that we keep healthy and fit. Smoking, alcohol and some drugs are very harmful to the body.

The drug nicotine is found in cigarettes. Cigarettes can seriously damage your health. People who smoke are at much greater risk of developing a disease that will kill them.

Some drugs can help us when we are ill. Others can be very dangerous. Drugs called antiseptics are used if we have an accident, such as cutting a finger.

If we drink too much alcohol as adults we can damage our livers and become very ill.

Certain drinks such as coffee and tea and some fizzy drinks contain caffeine. This makes your heart beat faster and keeps you awake. Too much can damage the wall of your stomach and put a strain on babies' hearts.

Answer these questions.

1   What drug is contained in cigarettes? ....

2   Name a drug that can help us when we are ill. ....

3   Which part of the body can we harm if we drink too much alcohol? ....

4   What is it in coffee that keeps you awake? ....

5   What does caffeine do to the heart? ....

6   What types of coffee only contain a small amount of caffeine? ....

7   Can people stop smoking? How? ....

....

Breathing

UNIVERSITY COLLEGE CHICHESTER
BOGNOR REGIS CAMPUS
UPPER BOGNOR ROAD
BOGNOR REGIS
WEST SUSSEX
PO21 1HR

We need oxygen to live and we get oxygen by breathing in air. Can you name the parts of the body we use to breathe?

Fill in the blanks using the words from the box.

nose	mouth
rib	diaphragm
windpipe	lung

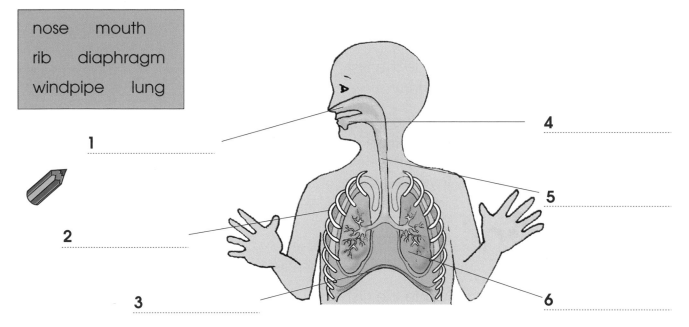

1 ....

2 ....

3 ....

4 ....

5 ....

6 ....

Complete the sentences by choosing words from the box below.

carbon dioxide	ribs	lungs	energy
blood	oxygen	waste	breathe

1   You have two [_____] which are connected with muscles and protected by your [_____].

2   As you breathe in you take in [_____]. It goes into your [_____] and then into your cells.

3   Inside the cells the oxygen is burnt to make [_____]. Waste is produced in the form of [_____] and water.

4   The [_____] is taken back into your lungs and got rid of as you [_____] out.

Discoveries and inventions

Look at this list of scientific discoveries. Fill in the correct scientist and date to go with each discovery.

		Scientist	Date
1	Discovered the spectrum		
2	Made the first battery		
3	Built the first steam train		
4	Invented the light bulb		
5	Discovered radium		
6	Made the first aeroplane		
7	Produced the first TV pictures		
8	Discovered penicillin		
9	Invented the jet engine		
10	Invented the hovercraft		

Cockerell 1959

Edison 1879   Fleming 1928   Wright brothers 1903

Curie 1898   Trevithick 1804   Newton 1672

Baird 1926   Whittle 1930   Volta 1800

Seeds

How much do you know about the life-cycle of a plant?

stamen

stigma

ovary

Before a flower can make any seeds it must be pollinated. This is done by bees or other insects. When an insect visits a flower, pollen sticks to it as it brushes against the stamen – the male part of the flower.

When the insect visits another flower, the pollen brushes onto the flower's stigma – the female part of the flower. **Pollination** then takes place. The pollen grain grows down to the ovary. If it gets inside the ovary, **fertilization** takes place and a seed is produced.

When the seeds are ready they are spread by the wind, water or by animals and birds. This is called **seed dispersal**.

The seeds fall onto the ground and **germinate** if the conditions are right. Some seeds take longer to germinate than others.

Answer these questions.

1   What are the four main stages in a plant's life?

....

2   What is pollination?

....

....

3   Which creatures do the pollinating? ....

4   What is the male part of the flower called? ....

5   What happens in the ovary?

....

6   How are seeds spread?

....

7   Why is the flower an important part of the plant?

....

Roots

The roots are a very important part of a plant. They take up water and nutrients from the soil.

fibrous
root

tap
root

There are two main types of root:

Fibrous roots go deep underground and spread out a long way.
Tap roots store food.

Which of the following plants have tap roots and which have fibrous roots?

1   Beetroot   ....

2   Turnip   ....

3   Daisy   ....

4   Runner bean   ....

5   Cabbage   ....

6   Swede   ....

7   Marigold   ....

8   Sunflower   ....

9   Lettuce   ....

10   Carrot   ....

Draw two different types of root system below.

Micro-organisms

Micro-organisms and bacteria can be useful. They can break down waste and make it harmless. But other bacteria can be harmful. They can cause disease and illness.

Soil has lots of tiny plants and creatures living in it – millions of micro-organisms that can only be seen with a microscope. These include algae and one-celled animals. When animals or plants die, the bacteria and decomposers in the soil act as 'dustmen'. Some micro-organisms can cause things to go mouldy and bad.

Answer these questions.

1   What happens to jam if it is left open to the air and not closed up?

    ....

2   What happens to a dead bird after several days if it is left?

    ....

3   Can some bacteria live in temperatures below zero?

    ....

4   What do bacteria use dead plants and animals for?

    ....

5   What happens to bread or cheese if it is left somewhere damp?

    ....

6   How many micro-organisms can be found in soil?

    ....

7   Name some animals that are decomposers.

    ....

    ....

    ....

    ....

Filtration

One way of separating substances is by using a filter. A filter is made of a material which has lots of tiny holes in it.

If you mix some chalk and water together and leave it for a long time it will separate. Another way to separate the two substances is to pour the mixture through a filter like this one.

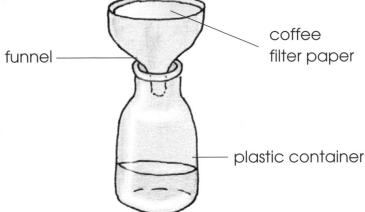

The chalk will stay in the filter and the water will pass through.

Mix up some sawdust and water.
Put this through a filter. What happens? ....

....

Now try sand and water. Is it easier to separate? ....

Try mixing other things together. Can they be separated using a filter?

Fill in the table below.

Substance	Can be separated using a filter?	
	Yes	**No**
Water and salt		
Water and gravel		
Water and flour		
Water and sugar		
Cooking oil and sand		
Cooking oil and chalk		

Switches

There are a number of different switches that you can make. Here are some.

On/Off switch

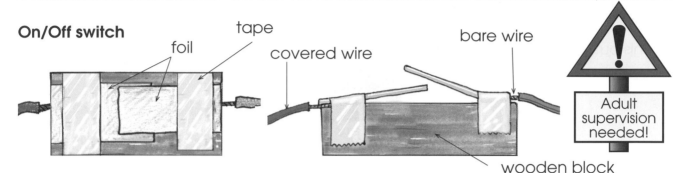

foil | tape | covered wire | bare wire | Adult supervision needed! | wooden block

Cover two pieces of card in foil. Fix to a small block of wood. Make sure that when the two pieces touch your circuit is completed.

Rotating switch

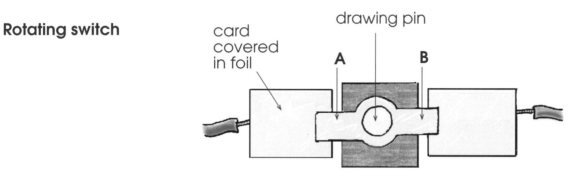

card covered in foil | drawing pin | A | B

Attach each end of the bare wire to a piece of card. Cut out another piece of card in this shape ⬤━◯━⬤ . Cover it in foil. Fix it to a piece of wood so that it spins freely. When the two ends of the switch **A** and **B** touch the card, they complete the circuit.

Two-way switch

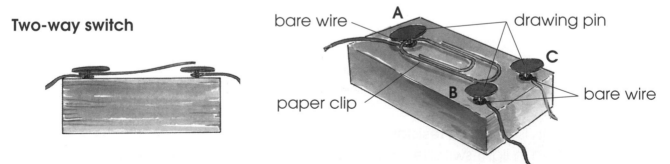

bare wire | A | drawing pin | C | paper clip | B | bare wire

Fix three drawing pins onto a small piece of wood. Fix a paper clip to one of the drawing pins. Bend it upwards. Press it down onto pin **B** to check your circuit. It can now be moved across so that it completes the circuit between **A** and **C**.

See what kinds of circuit you can make using the different switches. Try making a flashing light or intermittent buzzer, or even a lighthouse.

Dimmers

When you wind bare wire round a pencil and attach it to a circuit, you will make a dimmer for a light bulb. The longer the wire the more dimly the bulb will glow.

Try this out.

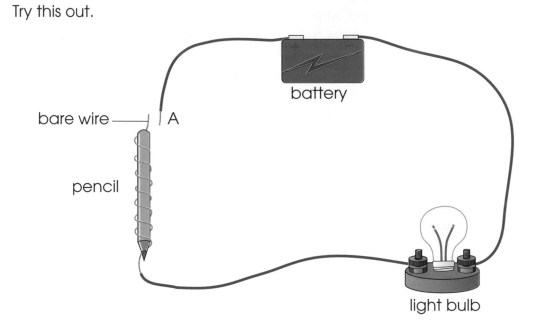

battery

bare wire —— A

pencil

light bulb

1   See if you can fit a switch into your circuit.

2   Take the end of wire **A** and touch it further down the pencil. Watch what happens to the bulb.
Write down what happened and why.

....

....

....

A dimmer like this is called a **resistor**.
Resistors are used in light switches and on the volume controls of radios.

3   Why do you think a dimmer is called a resistor?

....

....

Special circuits

Electric circuits can be wired up in two different ways.

Parallel circuit

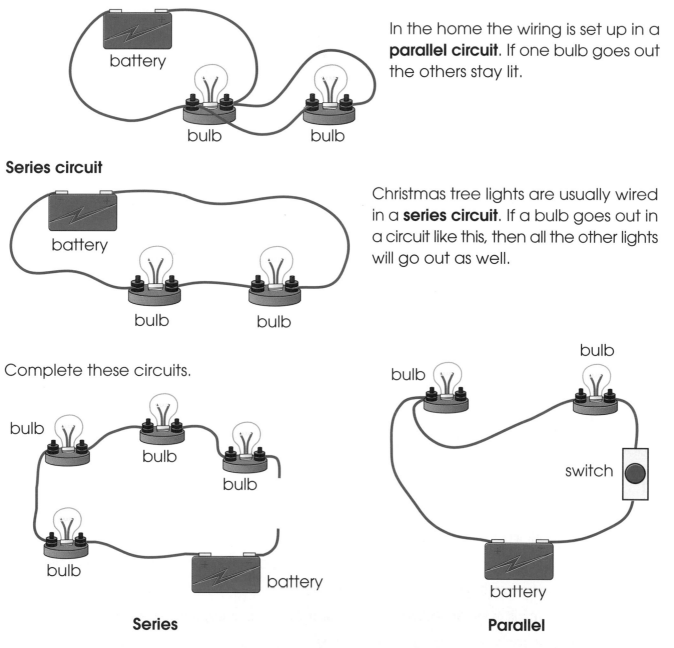

In the home the wiring is set up in a **parallel circuit**. If one bulb goes out the others stay lit.

Series circuit

Christmas tree lights are usually wired in a **series circuit**. If a bulb goes out in a circuit like this, then all the other lights will go out as well.

Complete these circuits.

Series

Parallel

Complete these sentences.

1   In a parallel circuit if one bulb goes out the others will ....

2   In a series circuit if one bulb goes out the others will ....

Forces

Forces work in pairs. When a gun is fired, the bullet leaves the gun forwards and the gun is pushed backwards.

If forces **balance** things will stay still.

a tower does not collapse

a bridge stands up

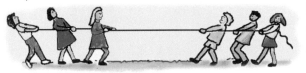

In a tug of war, if the two teams pull as hard as each other they will stay still.

If the forces become **unbalanced** things can speed up or change direction.

dropping a ball

hitting a ball

Force can be measured in newtons. The weight of 100 grams mass is about the same as 1 newton.

Underline the correct word from the brackets.

1   Force is measured in (grams, volts, newtons).

2   A tower will stay standing because the forces (balance, change, move).

3   Forces work in (threes, pairs, fours).

4   If a gun is fired, one force pushes the gun (sideways, forwards, backwards).

5   Things speed up if they are (still, dropped).

6   A tug of war is a good example of balanced (gravity, forces, friction).

7   A bridge stands up because the forces are (balanced, unbalanced, unequal).

8   Unbalanced forces can cause things to change (colour, direction, place).

9   200 grams mass is the same as (2, 10, 20) newtons.

10   A force can be called a push or a (turn, pull, stop).

Habitats

How are these creatures suited to their habitats?

1   fish/water

1 ....

2   mole/underground

2 ....

3   mountain goat/high areas

3 ....

4   polar bear/Arctic

4 ....

5   woodpecker/trees

5 ....

6   dolphin/sea

6 ....

7   camel/desert

7 ....

Planets

Look at this list of planets in our Solar System. Place them in the correct order, starting with the one closest to the sun.

Venus, Earth, Mars, Uranus, Saturn, Neptune, Pluto, Mercury, Jupiter

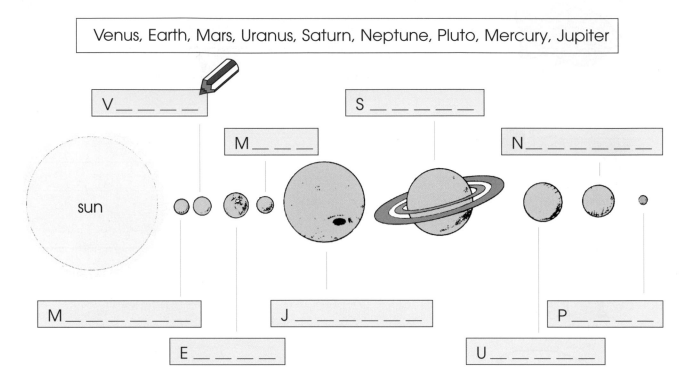

V _ _ _ _

S _ _ _ _ _ _

M _ _ _ _

N _ _ _ _ _ _ _

sun

M _ _ _ _ _ _ _

J _ _ _ _ _ _ _

P _ _ _ _ _

E _ _ _ _ _

U _ _ _ _ _ _

Now put the same planets in order of size with the smallest first.

1 ....   2 ....   3 ....

4 ....   5 ....   6 ....

7 ....   8 ....   9 ....

Answer these questions.

1 Is the sun a star or a planet? ....

2 Which planet is famous for its rings? ....

3 The Moon orbits which planet? ....

4 Which is the closest planet to the sun? ....

5 Which planet is furthest away from the sun? ....

6 Which planet is closest to the Earth? ....

Melting and boiling

The **melting point** is the temperature at which something melts or changes from a solid into a liquid. The **boiling point** is the temperature at which a liquid changes to a vapour.

> e.g.   The melting point of ice is 0°C or 32°F.
> The boiling point of water is 100°C or 212°F.

Other solids and liquids have different melting and boiling points.

What happens when you heat each of these solids? Does it melt? Write **yes** or **no**.

Solid	Does it melt?
Sugar	
Salt	
Wood	
Jelly	
Butter	
Clay	

Adult supervision needed!

Complete this chart.

solid — melt → liquid — boil →

ice cube   water

Use the words in the box to complete these sentences.

| boiling   melting   solid   liquid   vapour   ice   melts |

1   Solid water is called ....

2   A .... turns to a liquid at the .... point.

3   Ice .... at 0°C or 32°F.

4   Water turns to a .... at 100°C or 212°F.

5   A .... turns to a vapour at the .... point.

Make a periscope

A periscope is a device for seeing above things. Here is a simple way to make your own periscope.

Adult supervision needed!

With an adult, cut and fold a piece of stiff card as shown below. Stick the edges together. Slide two mirrors (11–12 cm wide) into the slots and use sticky tape to secure them.

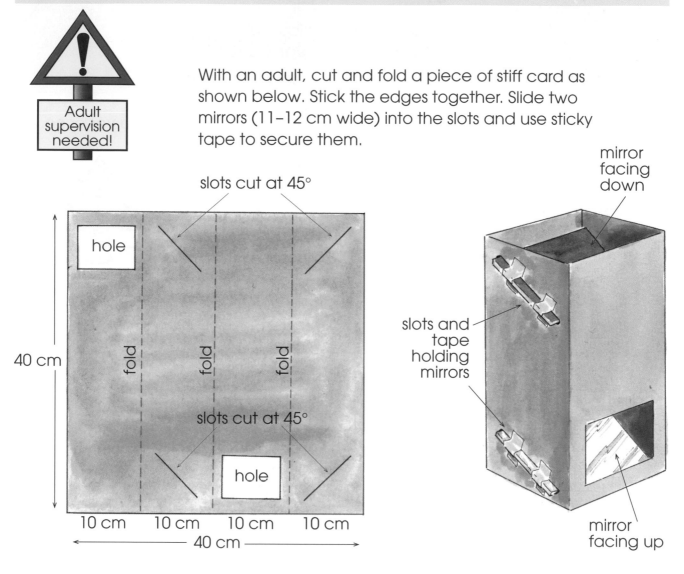

slots cut at 45°

hole

40 cm

fold fold fold

slots cut at 45°

hole

10 cm   10 cm   10 cm   10 cm

40 cm

mirror facing down

slots and tape holding mirrors

mirror facing up

It is important that the bottom mirror faces upwards and the top one faces downwards. The light will be reflected from the first mirror onto the second.

Using your periscope you will be able to see over people's heads and high fences. By turning the mirror round you will be able to see backwards.

Can you improve the design of your periscope?
By changing the design you may be able to use your periscope to look in different directions. See if you can make a device that will see round corners.

Being safe

1   Always wash your hands after handling plants and animals because ....

....

2   Never taste or smell unknown substances because ....

....

3   Always wear safety goggles if you are cutting things because ....

....

4   Never play with mains electricity because ....

....

5   Always keep plastic bags away from young children because ....

....

6   Be careful not to lift heavy objects because ....

....

7   Never try out gliders or kites near power lines because ....

....

8   Be careful with glass objects and mirrors because ....

....

9   Never play with household cleaning products because ....

....

10 Never look at the sun because ....

....

Ecological dangers

1   We go on buying more and more cars.

2   We continue to throw away more and more litter.

3   We pour sewage into the sea.

4   We chop down all the rainforests.

5   We overfish the sea.

6   We build more and more houses and factories.

7   We continue to fill our cars with petrol.

8   We pour chemicals into the rivers.

9   We continue to hunt animals for their fur and ivory.

10   We don't recycle glass, metal, paper and plastic.

Dissolving

Test out the following materials. Which will dissolve in cold water? Which will dissolve in warm water? Complete the chart below.

To test them out, fill a beaker one-third full with water. Add a tablespoon of the material. Find out how long each material takes to dissolve.

Try the same experiment but this time stir the solution.

Adult supervision needed!

Material	Will it dissolve in:		How long does it take in:	
	cold water	warm water	cold water	warm water
Sugar				
Flour				
Coffee				
Washing powder				
Salt				
Sand				
Icing sugar				
Powder paint				

Pulleys

Pulleys are used to make things move more easily. Using a pulley you can lift heavy weights.

This is a simple pulley.

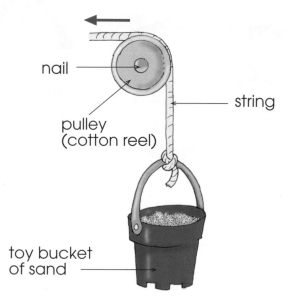

nail

string

pulley
(cotton reel)

toy bucket
of sand

Pull the rope (string) and the weight will lift upwards. If you use a double pulley you will need a piece of rope four times longer than your single pulley. You will need to pull the rope a little bit to lift the load.

What kind of things could you lift using a pulley system?

....

Fill in this chart using a single pulley.

Weight	How far do you have to pull the rope?	How far is the bucket lifted off the ground?
50 g		
100 g		
150 g		
200 g		
250 g		

Gears

Bicycles and cars are fitted with gears. Gears are special wheels that have teeth cut out. They each fit together. Gears can make small forces from large ones and large forces from small ones. The gears in a car will turn the engine of a car quickly, but the wheels will turn slowly. They are ideal for climbing a hill or slope.

Draw another smaller gear wheel to fit this one.

How many teeth have these two gear wheels?

Small one _____

Large one _____

Do the gears on these things make them go slower or faster? Tick the correct boxes.

	Slower	Faster	Both
Clock			
Car			
Bicycle			
Egg whisk			
Drill			

Draw a set of three different sized gear wheels, showing how they work together.

True or false

Which of these sentences are true and which are false? Tick the boxes.

		True	False
1	Carbon dioxide is a solid.	☐	☐
2	Water boils at 212°C.	☐	☐
3	Sodium chloride is the chemical name for salt.	☐	☐
4	Vinegar is an acid.	☐	☐
5	When iron is mixed with carbon it is called zinc.	☐	☐
6	Copper and silver are good conductors.	☐	☐
7	Plants give off oxygen.	☐	☐
8	Materials that do not allow light to pass through them are called transparent.	☐	☐
9	There are eight colours in the rainbow.	☐	☐
10	The greater the resistance in a circuit the brighter the bulb.	☐	☐
11	Sound waves can't be seen.	☐	☐
12	The bending of light when it passes from air to water is called reflection.	☐	☐
13	Gravity is the force that pulls things towards the Earth.	☐	☐
14	Salt can be separated from water by filtration.	☐	☐
15	Sound is measured in newtons.	☐	☐
16	There are eight notes in a musical octave.	☐	☐
17	Your eye is shaped like a tube.	☐	☐
18	We have about 206 bones in our bodies.	☐	☐
19	Plants will grow well if left in a dark, cold cupboard.	☐	☐
20	The Earth spins on its axis twice every day.	☐	☐

Noise

It is possible to cut out a lot of noise by using **insulation**.

Collect together an alarm clock, a small cardboard box and a selection of materials: sponge, rubber, newspaper, straw and polystyrene.

Put your alarm clock in the box. Set it to go off in 5 minutes. Close the lid and listen to the sound. Now try the same experiment but pack the box with newspaper. When the clock goes off is it any quieter? Try other materials and fill in the chart.

Insulation	Good	Bad
Newspaper		
Sponge		
Straw		
Rubber		
Polystyrene		

Which is the best insulation material?

....

Make your own ear muffs. Use thick card or wire, thin card and foam. Stick them together as shown with glue and tape.

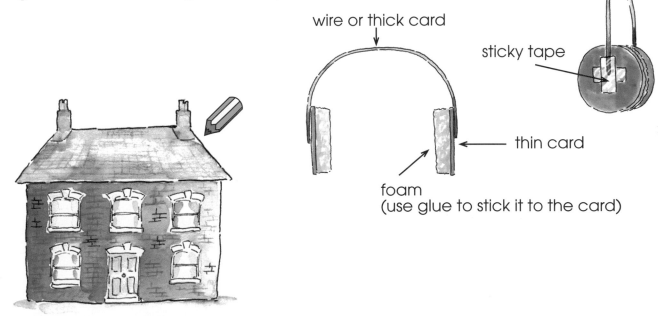

wire or thick card

sticky tape

thin card

foam
(use glue to stick it to the card)

Look at this house. Mark where the insulation might go. What is it used for?

....

Proteins

Through your life your body replaces old cells with new cells. To make the new cells you need different things. These include vitamins, minerals and protein.

Lots of foods contain protein, such as meat, fish and cheese.

You also get energy from protein. Look at the chart below. It shows how much of the vitamin C, protein and energy you need each day is given to you by these foods.

Foods	Vitamin C	Protein	Energy
Orange	225%	—	2%
Egg	—	12%	3%
Slice of brown bread	—	9%	5%
Baked beans on toast	16%	14%	6%
Glass of milk	12%	15%	8%
Jacket potato	100%	—	5%

Answer these questions.

1 How much energy will you get from an egg? ....

2 Will you get any vitamin C from an orange? ....

3 How much protein will you get from a slice of brown bread? ....

4 Which two things will give you the same amount of energy?

   ....

5 Will a jacket potato give you any protein? ....

6 How much vitamin C will you get from baked beans? ....

7 You will get 15% of protein from which food? ....

8 Which food on the list will give you the most energy? ....

Acids and alkalis

Some things behave in the same way and are put into groups. One group is called **acids**. Another is called **alkalis**. Some acids and alkalis are dangerous. They can burn and damage things. Others are not so dangerous and have many uses around the home.

Scientists test for acids and alkalis by using litmus paper. Acids turn litmus paper red and alkalis turn it blue.

To make your own acid/alkali tester, with an adult, boil some red cabbage in water. Pour off the purple liquid when it has cooled down. If you add an acid to this it will go red. If you add an alkali it will go blue. If the red cabbage water stays the same colour, the substance is called **neutral**.

Adult supervision needed!

Fill in this chart adding some of each substance to a little of your red cabbage water.

Substance	What colour does it turn the cabbage water?		
	Red (acid)	Blue (alkali)	Purple (neutral)
Lemon juice			
Vinegar			
Fizzy drink			
Toothpaste			
Milk of magnesia			
Bicarbonate of soda			
Sour cream			
Water			

Electromagnets

When you produce a magnet using an electric current it is called an **electromagnet**. It is very easy to make your own electromagnet.

Collect together a battery, two pieces of covered wire, a length of uncovered copper wire and a steel nail or bolt.

Wind the uncovered wire around the nail lots of times. The more times you do it the stronger your magnet will be.

Join the two ends of the electromagnet to a circuit.

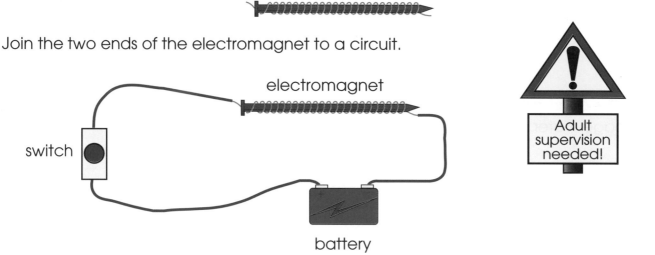

When you complete the circuit the magnet will work. See how far away a paper clip has to be from the magnet before it stops attracting it.

Electromagnets are used to sort scrap metal and other rubbish. They are used in electric bells, motors and loudspeakers.

Complete these sentences using the words from the box.

copper	electric	scrapyards	stronger	wire

1   Electromagnets are made using an .... current.

2   Electromagnets are used in ....

3   You must wind the .... around the nail or bolt many times.

4   The more turns the .... the magnet.

5   You should use .... wire to make your electromagnet.

Energy resources

List the advantages and disadvantages of these renewable energy resources.

| | Advantages | Disadvantages |

1   Solar panels

2   Windmills

3   Hydroelectric power

4   Wave machines

Bridges

People use different ways of crossing a river or gorge. One of these ways is by using a bridge.

There are three main types of bridge.

Arch

Suspension

Beam

Some bridges use two designs in one. An arch is used under a beam to give it extra strength. Bridges like this can often be seen on motorways.

When you build a bridge it is important to make sure that it is very strong.

See if you can make a bridge that will span a gap 20 cm wide using long straws, card and sticky tape. Use the straws underneath the card to give it extra strength. Here are some ideas you can use.

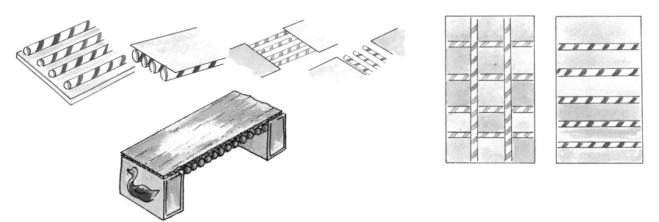

Test out the strength of your bridge. How much weight will your bridge take before it collapses? Which design was most successful?

If you increase the length of your bridge does it make any difference to the amount your bridge will hold?

When you have found the best design, build a model using your bridge. You could put a weight limit sign on one end. Try building your bridge using different types of material such as rolled up newspaper, corrugated cardboard or polystyrene.

Questionnaire

These questions can all be answered using this book.

1   Where can you feel your pulse?

2   Can smoking damage your health?

3   What do you take in when you breathe in?

4   Where does a pollen grain grow down to?

5   How do plants take in water?

6   How are a camel's feet suited to its habitat?

7   Where can resistors be used?

8   Who invented the light bulb?

9   Why are gears useful?

10   What is insulation?

11   Name two common acids.

12   Can you find vitamin C in oranges?

13   What do cigarettes contain that is dangerous?

14   What does caffeine do to you?

15   What is seed dispersal?

16   Name one way of separating substances.

17   How are Christmas lights usually wired?

18   Force is measured using which units?

19   Name one good form of sound insulation.

20   List three renewable energy resources.

21   What colour does an alkali turn litmus paper?

22   What does a plant use a tap root for?

23   Which is the largest planet in the Solar System?

24   What is the melting point of ice?

25   What are the three main types of bridge?

Answers

To Parents: We have not provided *all* the answers here. Some are examples only, as there are many possible correct answers. Use your judgement to see if your child's answer is a sensible alternative. Also, we have not given the answers to any practical activities. These will depend on the particular materials, etc, with which your child does the experiment, so they will need to be checked by you.

page 3

1 Smoking makes you cough and lose your breath. It gives you lung cancer. Smoking increases your heartbeat and blood pressure.
2 Carbon monoxide reduces the amount of oxygen in the blood.
3 Because cigarettes cause very harmful diseases that can kill you.

1 16   2 1965   3 300   4 $\frac{1}{4}$

page 4

1 nicotine   2 antiseptic   3 liver
4 caffeine   5 makes it beat faster
6 decaffeinated
7 Yes. By willpower, joining special groups and using special aids.

page 5

1 nose   2 rib   3 diaphragm
4 mouth   5 windpipe   6 lung

1 lungs, ribs   2 oxygen, blood
3 energy, carbon dioxide
4 waste, breathe

page 6

1 Newton 1672   2 Volta 1800
3 Trevithick 1804   4 Edison 1879
5 Curie 1898   6 Wright brothers 1903
7 Baird 1926   8 Fleming 1928
9 Whittle 1930   10 Cockerell 1959

page 7

1 pollination, fertilization, seed dispersal, germination
2 Pollination is when the insect takes the pollen and brushes it onto the stigma.
3 bees and other insects
4 the stamen
5 Fertilization – a seed is produced.
6 Seeds are spread by wind, water, animals and birds.
7 The flower attracts the insects.

page 8

1 tap   2 tap   3 fibrous   4 fibrous
5 fibrous   6 tap   7 fibrous   8 fibrous
9 fibrous   10 tap

page 9

1 It goes mouldy.
2 It will be attacked by bacteria and decomposers and start to break down.
3 Some die, others have their growth slowed down.
4 food   5 It goes mouldy.   6 millions
7 beetles, centipedes, maggots

page 12

2 The bulb should get brighter because the wire coil is shorter.
3 It is called a resistor because it makes it harder for the electricity to flow through the wire.

page 13

Series

Parallel

1 stay lit   2 go out

page 14

1 newtons   2 balance   3 pairs
4 backwards   5 dropped   6 forces
7 balanced   8 direction   9 2
10 pull

page 15

1 streamlined, fins and a powerful tail, gills
2 powerful front claws for burrowing, sensitive nose to feel for food, almost blind
3 warm coat, specially designed hooves, very agile and good sense of balance
4 thick fur and a lot of fat to keep warm, white coat blends in to help it stalk its prey
5 long pointed beak for pecking bark, strong claws to keep a good grip
6 streamlined, blow hole, uses high-pitched sounds to find its prey
7 hump stores fat, a lot of water stored in its stomach, thick eyelashes to protect eyes, large flat feet to stop it sinking

page 16

Mercury, Venus, Earth, Mars, Jupiter, Saturn, Uranus, Neptune, Pluto

1 Pluto   2 Mercury   3 Mars
4 Venus   5 Earth   6 Neptune
7 Uranus   8 Saturn   9 Jupiter

1 a star   2 Saturn   3 Earth
4 Mercury   5 Pluto   6 Mars

page 17

sugar – yes   salt – yes   wood – no
jelly – yes   butter – yes   clay – no
vapour/steam
1 ice   2 solid, melting   3 melts
4 vapour   5 liquid, boiling

page 19

1 they may carry germs or dirt.
2 they could be extremely dangerous and could kill you.
3 things could fly up and hit you in the face.
4 it could seriously hurt or even kill you.
5 they could suffocate.
6 you might hurt your back or drop the object.
7 they could become caught and the electricity would seriously hurt or kill you.
8 they could break and cut you.
9 they can be extremely poisonous or harmful.
10 it will damage your eyes.

page 20

1 We will increase the amount of fumes and pollution in the air.
2 It makes places untidy and unclean and can be harmful to wildlife.
3 It kills fish and other marine animals and pollutes our beaches.
4 It destroys the habitats of thousands of creatures. Trees are very valuable because they put oxygen back into the air.
5 There will be no more fish to eat.
6 We will use up all the countryside and land used for farming.
7 We will run out of oil.
8 We will poison the rivers and the creatures that live there will die.
9 Those animals will die out.
10 We will use more and more resources which will eventually run out.

page 23

clock – slower, car – both, bicycle – both, egg whisk – faster, drill – faster

page 24

1 false   2 false   3 true   4 true
5 false   6 true   7 true   8 false
9 false   10 false   11 true   12 false
13 true   14 false   15 false   16 true
17 false   18 true   19 false   20 false

page 25

The insulation should go in the roof and around the doors and windows. It is used to keep out noise and draughts.